Specimen Sight-Reading Tests for Oboe

Grades 1-5

The Associated Board of the Royal Schools of Music

GRADE 1

AB 2467

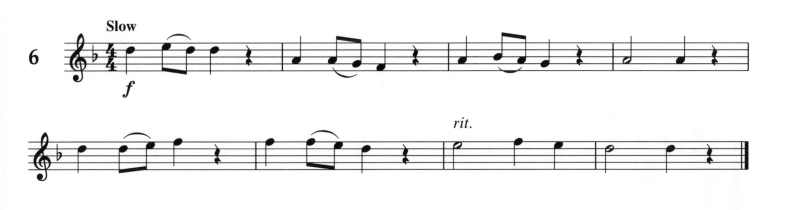

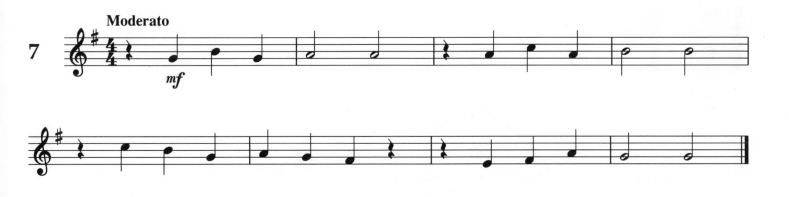

9 Lento

10 Moderato

11 Allegretto

Andante

15

Andante

16

Allegretto

17

Moderato

18

GRADE 2

13

14

15

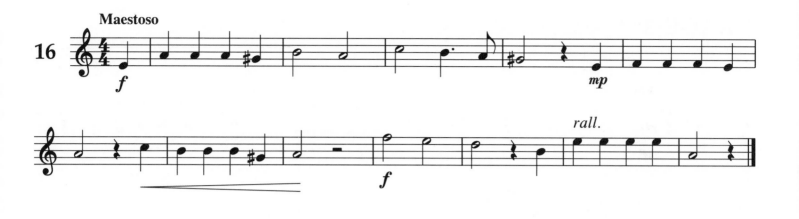

GRADE 3

5 Lento espressivo

6 Allegro delicato

7 Moderato

8 Allegro giocoso

GRADE 4

GRADE 5

4

5

6

AB 2467

Typeset by Musonix
Printed by Caligraving Limited, Thetford, Norfolk, England